REVISE KEY STAGE 2 SATs
English

TARGETED PRACTICE GRAMMAR

Series Consultant: Janice Pimm

Author: Helen Thomson

Also available:

Revise Key Stage 2 SATs English Targeted Practice
Spelling 9781292145969

Revise Key Stage 2 SATs English Targeted Practice
Reading 9781292145952

For the full range of Pearson revision titles, visit:
www.pearsonschools.co.uk/revise

Contents

Grammar

Punctuation

A small bit of small print

The Standards and Testing Agency publishes Sample Test Materials on its website. This is the official content and this book should be used in conjunction with it. The questions in this book have been written to help you practise what you have learned in your revision. Remember: the real test questions may not look like this.

Introduction

About your tests

At the end of Year 6, you will take tests to find out about your English skills. This book will help you revise your **grammar** skills.

- There will be one **grammar** test. This test will ask you questions about spelling, punctuation and grammar. You will have 45 minutes to do this test.

- You will also need to use your grammar skills to answer questions in the **reading** test. This test will ask you questions about some pieces of writing. You will have 1 hour to do this test.

There will be also be one **spelling** test. Your teacher will look at some of your pieces of **writing** but there won't be a writing test.

Using this book

Each page of this book is about a different skill. Use the checkboxes at the top of the page to track your progress:

Had a go ☐ Tick this box when you've had a go at the page.

Nearly there ☐ Tick this box when you understand the page quite well.

Nailed it! ☐ Tick this box when you understand the page really well.

Nouns

1. Underline all the nouns in the passage below. One has been done for you.

> It was a warm <u>evening</u> and the sun was just beginning to sink in the sky. The crows had gathered in the rookery high up in the trees on the edge of the village of Bishopthwaite. Their cawing resounded across the fields and rooftops as they flew back and forth fetching twigs and other materials for their nests. Simon was sitting on the gate watching them through his binoculars while he was talking.
>
> "Did you know that crows are supposed to be highly intelligent? Almost as intelligent as chimpanzees. My teacher told me that."

10 marks

2. Tick the sentences that contain proper nouns.

   a) Dubai is an amazing city but there is so much traffic. ☐

   b) Please put all the cups and plates in the sink. ☐

   c) Of all the musicians, Isabel is the most talented. ☐

   d) I found a book in the library on the topic of volcanoes. ☐

   e) I would love to be the first person to visit Mars. ☐

   3 marks

3. Complete the text with appropriate nouns.

> Remember, by nouns we mean the names of things. You can use any you want, so long as the text makes sense.

The cinema is on a busy ...., just a short .... from the .... centre. If you want to see a particular .... it is a good .... to book .... in advance, especially at the .... when it gets very busy. The best way to get there is to take a .... to the centre and then walk along the high .... If you are going by .... there is a .... park quite close by but you must remember to pay and get a ticket to display in the .... of your car or you will get a .... That would be a really nasty .... after coming out of the cinema and watching a good .... !   **7 marks**

Noun phrases

1. Circle all the noun phrases.
   One has been done for you.

> Remember, a noun phrase means a noun and any other words linked to it.

(a bucket)   leaping high   about now

the long, slithering snake   Come here now!

logging on   a microscopic amount   this mirror

3 marks

2. Underline the noun phrases in the sentences below.

   a) It was the time of the year that she loved.

   b) Breathing heavily, he ran up the very last hill in the race.

   c) Brilliant sunshine lit our way.

   d) The woman who met us at the station is my friend's aunt.   4 marks

3. Expand the noun phrases to make them more specific and add extra detail. One has been done for you.

> An expanded noun phrase is a noun phrase with extra detail.

   a) the cow **the large, munching Friesian cow** ....

   b) my rucksack ....

   c) the morning dew ....

   d) an old clock .... 3 marks

4. Write a description of your classroom, using at least five noun phrases.

   ....

   ....

   ....

   ....   5 marks

Pronouns

1. Circle all the pronouns that replace nouns in the passage below.

> Last weekend I went to the garden centre with my mum, sister Kate and baby brother
> Joseph. Mum wanted to buy geranium seedlings because she wants to grow them into
> larger plants and then plant them into flowering baskets when summer arrives. Kate and
> I like the section that sells tropical fish. We always look around it while Mum is choosing
> the plants. Joseph usually stays in his buggy but this time he wanted to come with us.
> Kate lifted him out of his buggy and we lifted him up to see the fish.

6 marks

Garden Centre

> Look for words
> that replace someone's
> name or a common noun.

2. Rewrite the passage below, replacing the underlined words with pronouns.

> Last summer, <u>my family and I</u> visited a pretty village by the sea called Clovelly.
> <u>Clovelly</u> was very busy because a lot of visitors like to go <u>to Clovelly</u>. The harbour was
> full of fishing boats. <u>My family and I</u> watched as <u>the fishing boats</u> sailed in and out.

....

....

....

....

....   **5 marks**

3. Underline the pronoun to match the noun in these sentences.
   One has been done for you.

   a) The clowns blew up balloons as *he/we/<u>they</u>* ran around the circus ring.

   b) The clouds look like they have faces on *it/them/her*.

   c) That cup has a chip on *us/her/it*.   **2 marks**

Possessive pronouns

1. Underline all the possessive pronouns in the passage.
One has been done for you.

> <u>My</u> cousin has bought a new bicycle. He has a Saturday job in a cycle repair shop and has been saving his wages for several months. I've also got a bike but it isn't as fast or as light as his. We often go for rides together at the weekend on our bikes. Last weekend his sister Tanya came too. Her bike isn't as fast as his but it is better than mine. We cycled to a café bar and left our bikes chained to the railings outside.

4 marks

2. Replace the noun and possessive apostrophe with the correct possessive pronoun.
One has been done for you.

> Possessive pronouns are words such as 'his' that tell us that something belongs to someone.

a) Margaret's shoes were badly worn.

Her shoes were badly worn.
....

b) Piotr's bag is under the table.

....

c) Dominic and Alice's mother is in hospital.

....   **2 marks**

3. Complete the sentences below with the correct possessive pronoun.
One has been done for you.

a) These are Jack's pens: they are **his.** ....

b) That is my garden: it's ....

c) This is Debbie's cat: it is ....

d) That car belongs to Ali and Ahmed: it is ....   **3 marks**

4. Write a short paragraph about your home, family or a friend, containing at least five examples of possessive pronouns.

....

....

....   **5 marks**   **4**

Relative pronouns

1. Complete the table with the words listed below.
One has been done for you.

> You use relative pronouns after a noun to make it clear which person or thing you are talking about. You also use them to add additional information.

| ~~who~~ | his | which | that | mine | ours | whose | theirs |

relative pronoun	possessive pronoun
who	

7 marks

2. Use the correct relative pronoun to complete each sentence.

a) My teacher, ... name is Mr Clare, is really funny.

b) In the Andalusian Mountains, ... wolves still roam, you can hike for miles.

c) Here is the shed .... my dad built.

d) We bought a camping stove, on .... we made tea.   **4 marks**

3. Underline the relative pronouns in the passage below.

My friend Harold, whom I saw last week, has an identical twin brother, whose name is Henry. They always wear the same clothes, which they choose together. Their favourite shop, where I first met Harold, is close to my house.

4 marks

4. Write a sentence containing a relative pronoun.

.... **1 mark**

Determiners

1. Circle the words below that are determiners.

> Determiners come before nouns and make the noun more specific.

| the | garage | an | this | determined | seven | every | your | how |

6 marks

2. Complete the passage below with the appropriate determiners.

.... only place where you can play netball in .... town

is at .... main sports centre. .... particular sports

centre has .... pitches and is floodlit in .... evening.

When I was there last week I met .... girl whom I knew from

.... school. She plays there .... week in a team called

.... Stars.   **5 marks**

3. Write a paragraph about your daily routine that contains at least five different types of determiner. Underline the determiners you use.

....

....

....

.... **5 marks**

4. Rewrite the passage below, including appropriate determiners so that it is grammatically correct.

Last Saturday we went to shopping mall in centre of town. Ben needed new trainers so we went into shop to look for them. Shop assistant said that they didn't have size.

I pointed to shoe shop next door and said, "Let's look in shop over there. It might have size."

....

....

....

.... **4 marks**   **6**

Conjunctions

1. Underline all the conjunctions in the
   text below. One has been done for you.

Conjunctions are
words that link different parts
of a sentence.

> Jade really wanted to go to the concert <u>because</u> her favourite band was playing
> but her parents said she could only go if she promised to get home before 9:00 pm.
> When we went online to book tickets at Jade's house we realised that the concert
> didn't finish until 9:30 pm so we couldn't go. Jade's bottom lip trembled, then she
> began to cry. Jade's mum came in and asked what the matter was. After we had
> explained, she said that if Jade's father collected us and brought us home when the
> concert had finished, Jade could go. Jade's father said that of course he would, so
> we bought tickets!

5 marks

2. Insert the correct conjunction to complete the sentences.

   a) Dad preheated the oven .... he was baking a cake.

   b) Oliver is great musician .... he's a dreadful singer.

   c) The woodland had an abundance of wildlife including muntjac deer
   .... badgers.

   d) My grandmother lent me some money .... I was able to have
   dancing lessons.   **4 marks**

3. Complete each sentence with a phrase containing a conjunction.
   One has been done for you.

   a) I bought a bunch of beautiful, yellow lilies **because they smelt so fragrant.**

   b) My sister is a very strong swimmer ....

   c) Bharesh's laptop was running out of battery ....

   d) A new planet has been discovered at the edge of our solar system

   ....

   3 marks

Prepositions

1. Which of the sentences contains a preposition?

> Prepositions are used to show time, place or direction.

Tick **one.**

   a) The elves played flutes and danced.   ☐

   b) Carlos has two brothers and a sister.   ☐

   c) The canal boat sailed under the bridge.   ☐

1 mark

2. Underline the preposition in each sentence.

   a) The rabbits were running through the undergrowth.

   b) We went ice skating before dinner.

   c) There is a bowling alley inside the arcade.

   d) The path runs along the top of the cliff.

   e) Our art teacher plays music during the lesson.

5 marks

3. Complete the table with examples of prepositions of time, place and direction. One of each has been done for you.

time	place	direction
until	next to	into

6 marks

4. Write a sentence containing a preposition of direction.

....

....

....

.... 1 mark

Adjectives

1. Complete the table with the words listed below.
   One has been done for you.

   > Adjectives are used to describe nouns.

   | afternoon | pastry | heavenly | loud | weather | lovely |

adjective	noun
	afternoon

   5 marks

2. Are the statements true or false? Tick one box in each row.

	true	false
Adjectives always come before a noun.		
Adjectives make text more interesting.		
You can only use one adjective to describe a noun.		

   3 marks

3. Rewrite the sentences and make them more interesting by including at least one appropriate adjective. One has been done for you.

   a) We met a man at the crossroads by the petrol station.

   <u>We met a tiny, frail, old man at the crossroads by the petrol station.</u>

   b) Shelley made a cake for tea.

   ....

   c) The gorillas were in an enclosure in the centre of the wildlife park.

   ....

   d) The sunset spread across the hills.

   ....

   ....

   e) The trombone was in the music room.

   .... **4 marks**

Present and past progressive tenses

1. Tick the sentences that are written in the present tense.

> The tense of a verb tells you when it is happening.

We are entering our Cocker Spaniel into a pet show tomorrow. ☐

My sleeping bag got wet when we went camping. ☐

Ted's favourite sport is judo. ☐

I have finished my homework. ☐

They are running onto the pitch. ☐

2 marks

2. Which of the sentences in Question 1 is in the present progressive? Copy the sentence out below.

> You use the present progressive tense to talk about something that is happening at the moment you are speaking.

....   **1 mark**

3. Draw lines to match each sentence to the correct tense.

sentence	tense
The vehicles were boarding the ferry.	simple present
He isn't in school today.	simple past
The Tasmanian tiger became extinct in 1936.	present progressive
The luggage is coming down the conveyor belt now.	past progressive

4 marks

4. Write a sentence including an example of the past progressive tense.

....

....   **1 mark**

Perfect tense

1. Tick the sentence in the present perfect form.

Tick **one**.

> The perfect form always uses the past participle.

a) The band completed their tour last month. ☐

b) The band has just completed their tour. ☐

c) The band will have completed their tour next month. ☐

1 mark

2. Underline the correct verb form to complete each sentence.

a) *Have you/Did you completed your homework yet?*

b) *The coal mines have closed/closed many years ago.*

c) *My aunt has bought/bought a table in an auction last week.*

3 marks

3. Circle the correct time expression to complete the sentences.

a) Our team has scored three goals *in the last match/so far/yet.*

b) Year 6 had an art lesson *already/before lunch/since yesterday.*

c) Grandpa told me about his childhood *when he came to stay/ already/since I was young.*

3 marks

4. Draw lines to match each sentence with its correct tenses. One has been done for you.

sentence		tense
Tom borrowed a towel.		future perfect
Tom will have borrowed a towel.		past perfect
Tom had already borrowed a towel.		present perfect
Tom has borrowed a towel.		simple past

3 marks

Auxiliary verbs

1. Circle all the auxiliary verbs in the sentences.
   One has been done for you.

   > Auxiliary verbs support the main verb. The three most common are forms of the verb **be, do** and **have.**

   a) We (are) having supper later this evening.

   b) Do you like vindaloo curry? Yes, I do.

   c) She doesn't like to be seen with uncombed hair.

   d) Did you arrive before everyone else?

   e) Dad said that he might build a tree-house for us.

   f) They were watching television at home at the time.   7 marks

2. Find the auxiliary verbs in the word search below.
   There are eight to find.

a	s	x	h	d	o
m	r	v	y	i	s
f	b	e	l	d	m
v	d	x	c	a	n
h	a	s	r	m	o

   8 marks

3. Write five sentences below, using examples of auxiliary verbs from the word search.

   ....

   ....

   ....

   ....

   ....   5 marks

12

Modal verbs

1. Circle the modal verbs in the sentences.

> Modal verbs are a type of auxiliary verb. They are used in front of the main verb and are used to show possibility, obligation or necessity.

a) We might see the humpback whales if we are lucky.

b) Suleiman can hold his breath underwater for 65 seconds.

c) You should make an appointment with the dentist immediately if you have toothache.

d) She is very kind and would give away all her money if she had any. **4 marks**

2. Number the sentences from 1 to 4 to show how likely it is that the band will release a new record this year. One has been done for you.

The band might release a new record this year.	
The band will release a new record this new.	1
The band ought to release a new record this year.	
The band could release a new record this year.	

3 marks

3. Draw lines to show whether these sentences show possibility, obligation or necessity.

You should save up to make sure you have enough money for the holidays.

We must get to Dover before the ferry leaves.

My laptop crashed so it might not work anymore.

possibility

obligation

necessity

4. Write a paragraph advising a visitor to your town. Use modal verbs to advise them on what they should and shouldn't do.

....

....

....

....

.... **5 marks**

Subjunctive verb forms

1. **Which of the below sentences are in the subjunctive form?**

Tick **two.**

> The subjunctive form is used to express possibility or uncertainty, and importance or urgency. It is mainly used in formal language.

I suggest that she leave at the earliest opportunity.   ☐

The ice-cream van will arrive when school finishes.   ☐

The school expects that all pupils be fully dressed in school uniform.   ☐

Gladys is growing geraniums in pots.   ☐

2 marks

2. **Circle the correct verb to complete the sentence in the subjunctive form. One has been done for you.**

a) My mother requested that I *am*/(*be*) allowed to take a day off school to visit my gran in hospital.

b) It is recommended that the patient *remain*/*remains* in hospital for at least another week.

c) If it *were*/*was* practical to build a tree-house we would.   **2 marks**

3. **Rewrite the sentences below using the subjunctive form.**

a) It is important that she brushes her teeth every day.

....

b) The headmaster makes everyone wear a tie.

....

c) Do we have to attend too?

....

d) He must remember to do his exercises every day.

....   **4 marks**

Adverbs

1. Tick one box in each row to show whether the underlined word is an adjective or an adverb.

sentence	adjective	adverb
He is <u>never</u> late.		
This is a <u>perfect</u> example of paintings from that era.		
Harminder has <u>mysteriously</u> disappeared.		
It is a <u>total</u> mystery.		

4 marks

2. Underline all the adverbs in the passage below.

It was a perfectly still day, ideal for a lazy afternoon boating on the lake. Alek, Louise and I slowly wandered along the meandering paths through the long rushes, listening to the moor hens occasionally calling from their nests.

We eventually arrived at the pontoon. The rowing boat was still securely tied up where we had left it last summer. It looked as if no one had even been there since our visit. We eagerly hopped on board, throwing our fishing rods onto the wooden seats and picking up the creaky, old oars, then rowed swiftly out into the middle of the lake. It was only then that we noticed the crack – a huge, gaping crack in the bottom of the boat. How could we not have seen it when we had blindly jumped aboard? As the water began rapidly to pour in, the afternoon's peace was abruptly shattered by Alek's screams of fear.

5 marks

3. Rewrite each sentence, using an adverb to describe the action. One has been done for you.

a) "I'm exhausted," he said in a weary voice.

    "I'm exhausted," he said **wearily**.
    ....

b) I'm sure it wasn't deliberate of Marsha to kick him.

    ....

c) She is a graceful dancer.

    ....

d) The crowd gave a defiant shout.

.... 3 marks

Adverbials

1. Underline the adverbials in each of the sentences. One has been done for you.

> Adverbials are adverbs or phrases that give more detail about a verb. They can describe when, where or how something happens.

   a) The owl flew <u>into a crumbling, abandoned barn.</u>

   b) She ran outside in a tremendous hurry.

   c) Once we had finished the picnic, we cleared away the remaining food.

   d) The clock struck on the stroke of midnight.

   e) Fiercely guarding her cubs, the lioness prowled the territory.   **4 marks**

2. Tick one box in each row to show whether the underlined adverbial describes when, where or how something happens.

	when	where	how
The children were screeching with laughter <u>at the back of the room</u>.			
The wolves began to howl <u>as the sun went down</u>.			
<u>With a sudden roaring of the engine</u>, the racing car roared around the bend.			

3 marks

3. Which of the sentences below contains a fronted adverbial?

Tick **one.**

   a) The ships were sailing into the harbour. ☐

   b) We were on holiday when we heard the great news. ☐

   c) They camped out under a full moon. ☐

   d) Just as I was falling asleep, the alarm clock rang. ☐

   1 mark

4. Write three sentences containing adverbials to show where, when and how something happens.

....

....

....   **3 marks**

16

Questions and statements

1. Punctuate the sentences correctly. Each should end in either a full stop or a question mark.

   Statements and questions are forms of sentences. A complete sentence must contain a subject and a verb.

   a) What is the longest river in Britain

   b) He can't be right all of the time can he

   c) Nightingales are quite common in the woodland around here   3 marks

2. Underline the subject and verb in each sentence.

   a) Chang loves to ski.

   b) The ponies came galloping round the ring.

   c) Did the caretaker change the light bulbs?   3 marks

3. Change these sentences into tag questions. One has been done for you.

   a) It's going to be the hottest day of the year today.

   It's going to be the hottest day of the year today, isn't it?
   ....

   b) Ali was born on a Friday.

   ....

   ....

   c) Dame Kelly Holmes is a world renowned athlete.

   ....

   ....   2 marks

4. Write two sentences. Make one sentence a statement and the other a question expressing surprise.

   ....

   ....

   ....

   ....   2 marks

Commands and exclamations

1. Decide if these sentences are commands or exclamations by underlining the correct choice. Then write the sentences with the correct punctuation.
One has been done for you.

   a) Stop that noise now (<u>command</u>/exclamation)

   Stop that noise now!
   ....

   b) Cut out the mask and paint it in bright colours (command/exclamation)

   ....

   c) Bring my shoes back here immediately (command/exclamation)

   ....

   d) What a clever dog he is (command/exclamation)

   ....

   3 marks

2. Use the words below to write commands and exclamations. Use exclamation marks where appropriate. One has been done for you.

   > Another word for command is imperative. We sometimes call them 'bossy' verbs because they are used to give people orders.

   a) what/fantastic/surprise

   What a fantastic surprise it is!
   ....

   b) bring/fire extinguisher/immediately

   ....

   c) place/ingredients/bowl/mix well

   ....

   d) how/scary/would be/get lost/here

   ....

   3 marks

Subject and object

1. Circle the subjects in the sentences.

   a) Poppy threw all her toys out of the pram.

   b) They rode their bicycles into town.

   c) She gave the prize away.

> In a sentence or clause the **subject** is the person or thing who is doing something and the **object** is the person or thing who is having something done.

3 marks

2. Underline the objects in the sentences.

   a) Harmeet put the cups on the table.

   b) She adores the puppies.

   c) The greenhouse keeps the plants warm.

   3 marks

3. Are the underlined words in each sentence the subject or object?
   Tick one box in each row.

	subject	object
Tola has lost her <u>ballet shoes</u>.		
<u>We</u> put the lovely picture in a frame.		
Zac patted <u>the horse</u>.		
The builders are working on <u>the extension to the school</u>.		
<u>I</u> did it!		

5 marks

4. Tick two sentences in which the subject and verb agree.

Tick **two.**

Many of my friends loves playing football. ☐

Everyone is going to the carnival. ☐

The woman live near the airport. ☐

Children under 16 are not allowed to play the lottery. ☐

The cats is sleeping on the bed. ☐

2 marks

Phrases

1. Tick to show which of the groups of words below are phrases. One has been done for you.

> A phrase is a group of words that doesn't contain a verb and a subject actively doing something. Phrases are usually parts of sentences.

	phrase
A stitch in time	✓
The riders galloped over the plain	
Many hands make light work	
An arm and a leg	
The long road home	
I'm running	

2 marks

2. Underline the phrases in the sentences. One has been done for you.

   a) It is important to stay in touch <u>for the sake of an old friendship.</u>

   b) Those doughnuts look delicious, with all that jam.

   c) I can smell the sea air; there's nothing nicer.

   d) My dad's formed a band with his pals, what a laugh!

   e) There is a buffet laid out on the table.

   f) It will happen, all in good time.

5 marks

3. Complete the sentences with the phrases listed below.

out of nowhere	on top of everything else	how cool

   a) This is too much work ....

   b) He arrived ....

   c) He's gone snowboarding: ....   **3 marks**

Clauses

1. Tick one box in each row to show if the following are clauses or phrases. One has been done for you.

> A clause is a group of words containing a verb and a subject actively doing something.

	phrase	clause
As the rainbow reached across the sky,		✓
In deep trouble,		
Although the skate park is now closed,		
After the storm		
On the trail of a deer		

4 marks

2. Underline the clauses within these sentences. One has been done for you.

a) Until very recently, <u>I had never been to the theatre</u>.

> A clause makes sense on its own.

b) In spite of the weather, we had an amazing time.

c) Ethan stayed awake until ten o'clock, despite being tired.

d) Despite the sugar content, strawberry smoothies are a tasty snack.

e) I love reading in whatever form, electronic books or paperbacks.

f) Matilde loves playing golf, even in the rain.

5 marks

3. Write a paragraph about what you do at the weekend. Include at least three examples of clauses.

....

....

....

....

4 marks

Main and subordinate clauses

1. Underline the main clause and circle the subordinate clause in each sentence. One has been done for you.

> Main clauses make sense on their own but subordinate clauses do not.

a) <u>Dragons stories can seem very real to small children,</u> (although they are only myths)

b) Whenever it snows, the whole community gathers at the top of the hill to go sledging.

c) That family is very happy, despite the weather.

d) I love lilac flowers because they have a beautiful fragrance.

e) If I were older, I would go travelling alone.   **4 marks**

2. Draw lines to match each main clause with a subordinate clause.

main clause	subordinate clause
Sam called out to his mum	while being coaxed to stand up.
The camels moaned and bared their teeth	even though he has fat fingers.
Noah is a talented pianist	until it takes place.
Mia had lunch	as she turned to go.
We won't know whether the play is good or not	before leaving the house.

5 marks

3. Rewrite the sentences that you made in Question 2, putting the subordinate clause at the beginning. Don't forget that you need a comma between the clauses when the subordinate clause comes first. One has been done for you.

a) As she turned to go, Sam called out to his mum.
....

b) ....

c) ....

d) ....

e) ....   **4 marks**

Coordinating conjunctions

1. **Underline the coordinating conjunctions in the sentences. One has been done for you.**

   > Coordinating conjunctions join together clauses that are of equal importance (main clauses).

   a) Yusef loves hockey <u>but</u> he hates football.

   b) He can't swim yet he still comes to the pool.

   c) We were very tired so we went to bed.

   d) All the books have been sold and the shop is not going to stock any more.

   e) The travellers could take the ferry or they could go through the Channel Tunnel.

   4 marks

2. **Find seven coordinating conjunctions in the word search.**

a	x	c	n	k	a	a
z	n	t	o	r	w	b
q	g	d	r	u	l	u
l	f	x	e	y	e	t
z	s	m	f	y	v	p
f	o	r	c	l	q	p

   7 marks

3. **Complete these sentences with the most appropriate coordinating conjunction.**

   a) The dog looks very cute .... it isn't very friendly.

   b) It was very cold .... Grandma lit the log-burner.

   c) Would you like to eat in the kitchen .... would you prefer a picnic in the garden?

   d) Erin travelled by train to London .... then she took the underground to Buckingham Palace.

   4 marks

4. **Write a sentence using a coordinating conjunction.**

.... **1 mark**

Subordinating conjunctions

1. Circle the subordinating conjunctions in the sentences. One has been done for you.

   > Subordinating conjunctions are words that introduce a subordinate clause within a sentence. They can be a single word or a group of words.

   a) We didn't stay until the end (even though) it was great.

   b) Ruth watched a film until it got dark.

   c) We lit the candles because the power cut was still on.

   d) They danced on the beach while the sun went down.

   e) Toby remembers his grandfather whenever he hears that song.   **4 marks**

2. Which of these sentences contain either coordinating conjunctions or subordinating conjunctions? Underline the conjunction and tick the correct box. One has been done for you.

	coordinating conjunction	subordinating conjunction
The colt rested under the tree <u>while</u> the mare grazed.		✓
The Republic of Ireland is part of the British Isles but it isn't part of the United Kingdom.		
Would you like to go ice skating or would you prefer to go bowling?		
Although there are penguins in the Antarctic there are none in the Arctic.		
We will paint the shed once it has been built.		
The ducklings hatched while we watched.		

5 marks

3. Write a sentence containing a subordinating conjunction.

   ....

   ....   **1 mark**

Relative clauses

1. Circle the nouns in the sentences and underline the relative clauses. One has been done for you.

> A relative clause gives you more information about a noun. It always comes after the noun.

   a) The new (Wembley Stadium), <u>which was built in 2007,</u> stands on the site of the original one.

   b) Amena, who is seven years old, has a brother called Marwan.

   c) Paris, where the Eiffel tower is located, is the capital of France.

   d) The restaurant at the end of the road, which is run by the Chen family, serves delicious noodles.

   3 marks

2. Draw lines to match the sentences with the correct relative pronoun. One has been done for you.

   Aunt Flora, ... retired last year, spends a lot of time doing yoga.   whose

   The mangrove swamps, ... you can find in Florida, are the habitat of alligators.   where

   Yvonne Taylor, ... son is a famous singer, lives next door to us.   who

   In the woodland, ... the bluebells grow, there's a little Shepherd's hut.   which

   3 marks

3. Complete each sentence by creating a relative clause that makes sense.

   a) The Eurovision Song Contest, ..., has contestants from all around the world.

   b) Michael's teacher, ..., is very patient.

   c) Spain, ..., is a great place for a holiday.

   d) David, ..., also has a grandfather who is 95 years old.

   e) The bungalow on the next street, ..., has a lovely front porch.

   5 marks

Active and passive

1. Tick one box in each row to show if the sentences are in the active or passive voice. One has been done for you.

> The active and passive voice are two ways of saying the same thing but in a different tone.

	active	passive
The nuts were eaten by the monkeys.		✓
The bank opens at nine o'clock.		
Dinner is served in the restaurant.		
The racers are approaching the finishing line.		
A window was broken last night when everyone was in bed.		

4 marks

2. Rewrite the sentences and put them in the passive tense. One has been done for you.

a) The tree surgeons felled the overhanging trees.

   <u>The overhanging trees were felled by the tree surgeons.</u>

b) Helena trimmed Emma's hair.

   ....

c) Boris mended the hole in the wall.

   ....

d) Rahman tied the little boy's shoe laces.

   ....   3 marks

3. Imagine you are the witness to a small collision between two cars. Write a paragraph explaining what happened, using examples of the passive voice.

> The passive voice is used frequently in formal language so is appropriate for report writing.

   ....

   ....

   ....

   ....   5 marks

Past tense

1. Underline all the examples of the past tense in the passage below. One has been done for you.

> There are several different forms of the past tense.

It <u>was</u> a very ordinary day. Jed even said that it had been an extremely long, boring day. One of the most boring days he could remember – until it happened. He and Lindon had travelled together on the number 16 bus as they always did. Jed gets on two stops before Lindon and always saves a seat for him at the back. Jed was aimlessly playing with his phone when Lindon got on. School that day was much the same as any on a wet Wednesday in November. There were the usual reprimands from Mr Johnson when hardly anyone had done their homework.

"I have told you a million times – you are not going to pass this exam by playing video games all evening!"

The two boys ambled through the school gate at four o'clock as usual. Instead of catching the bus they decided to walk home through the woodland at the back of school. As they were coming into the small clearing in the centre they became aware of a humming noise. They looked up, and there it was! An immense spacecraft was taking off over the treetops.

9 marks

2. Find examples of these tenses in the passage above.

a) The past perfect tense

....

b) The simple past tense

....

c) The present perfect tense

....

d) The past progressive tense

.... 4 marks

3. Write a sentence with an example of the past perfect tense.

.... 1 mark

Future tense

1. Circle all the examples of the future tense in the passage below.

> There are several different ways of forming the future tense.

My friend Jennifer is really excited because her dog Smudge is going to have puppies very soon. Smudge is a Golden Labrador but Smudge's mother had black fur so Jennifer doesn't know if the puppies will be golden or black. She is hoping that Smudge will have a large litter and that some of the puppies will be golden and that some will be black.

I asked Mum and Dad if we could have one of the puppies. Mum said she would have to think about it. Jennifer told me that the puppies will be eight weeks old when they go to their new homes.

6 marks

2. Tick the sentences that express the future tense.

	future tense
We are having muffins for breakfast this Sunday.	
He has taken up judo.	
The washing up will have been done before Mum gets home.	
The swimming pool closed at nine o'clock.	
You will recognise us because we will be wearing purple T-shirts.	

3 marks

3. Write a paragraph about your plans for something which will happen in the future. This could be a holiday or what you plan to do next weekend. Include at least one example of the future perfect tense.

....

....

....

....

....   **3 marks**

Standard English

1. Tick one box in each row to show whether the sentences are written in Standard or non-Standard English.

> You would use 'Standard' or 'formal' English in situations such as official reports or formal letters. 'Chatty' language or dialect can't be used in formal language.

	Standard English	non-Standard English
Hiya, how are you doing?		
It has been a pleasure to meet you.		
They've grabbed the ball and legged it.		
Please ensure that all the trays are cleared away.		
I insist that she take the money, she has been most helpful.		

5 marks

2. Circle the correct phrase in the brackets to complete the sentence in formal English. One has been done for you.

   a) Please *give a bell to/(contact)* the manager to find out more information.

   b) *Do you have/have you got* enough time to complete this?

   c) *You must/Pupils are expected to* wear trainers or soft shoes in the sports hall.

   d) *I have been informed/Someone told me* that the Prime Minister is visiting the town.

   3 marks

3. Rewrite the sentences in Standard English.

   a) It wasn't me who nicked the sweets.

   ....

   b) He ain't going on holiday cause his brother's ill.

   ....

   c) The shop keeper told everyone to clear off out of his shop.

   ....   3 marks

Capital letters and full stops

1. **Underline each word that should start with a capital letter in the sentences below.**

   > You use capital letters to start a sentence, for proper nouns and for the personal pronoun I.

   a) In march 1965, mrs beryl thornberry swam across the english channel to france.

   b) i have invited lucas, ben and niamh to my party – i hope they can come.

   c) london is the capital of england and rome is the capital of italy.   **8 marks**

2. **Tick one box in each row to show if the statement is true or false.**

statement	true	false
A person's title and name need capital letters.		
Unless they start a sentence, proper nouns don't need capital letters.		
You use a capital letter to start a new sentence.		

   3 marks

3. **Add full stops and capital letters to the passage below. One has been done for you.**

   > Most sentences are statements that end in a full stop. Remember, a sentence contains a clause (subject and verb) or a number of linked clauses.

   > **M**
   > I have swimming on monday and football on
   >
   > thursday so i am not available then i can do
   >
   > wednesday unless my sister has her french class

   7 marks

4. **Explain why this sentence is incorrect. Give two reasons.**

   my friend saw the new bond film she said it was awful

   ....

   ....

   2 marks

Question marks and exclamation marks

1. Draw lines to label each sentence as a statement, question or exclamation.

> Questions and exclamations are both types of sentences but they are punctuated by question marks and exclamation marks.

We always put glass bottles in the recycling bin.		question
What a fun party that was!		statement
How big is the population of Cardiff?		exclamation

3 marks

2. Decide if the sentences are statements, questions or exclamations and then punctuate them correctly.

   a) What an amazing painting this is

   b) Tokyo is the capital of Japan

   c) Do you like mangoes   6 marks

3. Rewrite the sentences as tag questions and punctuate them correctly. One has been done for you.

   a) You've got a younger brother.

   You've got a younger brother, haven't you?................................

   b) They visited Poland during the holidays.

   ....

   c) Alan is very kind.

   .... 2 marks

4. Write examples of a sentence, a question and an exclamation.

   ....

   ....

.... 3 marks

Commas in lists

1. Punctuate the sentences correctly by adding commas. One has been done for you.

> Commas are used to separate different things in a list. These could be nouns, adjectives or verbs.

a) The rainforest is full of animals: there are boa constrictors, sloths, tapirs and spider monkeys.

b) We took old pots and pans clothes bottles jars and newspapers to the recycling centre.

c) Dobry can play tennis football basketball and hockey.

d) It was a cold dark depressing grey day in January.   **3 marks**

2. Read Diana's shopping list and then complete the sentence below, using the correct punctuation.

Shopping list

a litre of milk

six eggs

a tin of beans

one grapefruit

a loaf of bread

Diana is going to buy a litre of milk ....

....

.... **1 mark**

3. Rewrite the sentence, adding two adjectives to describe each noun. Remember to punctuate your answer correctly.

There is a peacock on the lawn.

....

.... **1 mark**

Commas for clarity

1. Punctuate the sentences with commas so that the meaning is clear.

   a) I love riding tortoises ice-cream bicycles and swimming.

   b) Let's eat Billy!

   2 marks

2. Tick one box to show the correctly punctuated sentence.

   Tick **one.**

   Swiftly closing the door, behind her Bryony ran into the garden. ☐

   Swiftly closing the door behind her, Bryony ran into the garden. ☐

   Swiftly closing the door behind her Bryony, ran into the garden. ☐

   1 mark

3. Read each sentence and work out why commas have been used.
   Draw lines to match each sentence to the correct reason.

sentence	reason
Caitlin, who has huge feet, is really good at water skiing.	To mark the end of a fronted adverbial.
After a massive lunch, everyone fell sound asleep.	To mark the end of a subordinate clause.
Although we concentrated hard, we still couldn't work out what was happening.	To mark the start and end of a relative clause.

   3 marks

4. Insert commas into the sentences to mark out the relative clauses.
   One has been done for you.

   a) The elephants, which were in the enclosure near the entrance, had their young with them.

   b) Javier who comes from Spain can speak three languages.

   c) The Canadian state of Ontario where you can visit the Niagara Falls is heavily forested in some areas.

   2 marks

Parenthesis

1. Tick one box to show which of these sentences is correctly punctuated.

> Parenthesis is used to include extra information in a sentence and is marked by brackets, dashes or commas. The sentence will still make sense if the parenthesis is taken out.

Tick **one.**

The Netherlands, which is famous for its beautiful tulips, is a very flat country. ☐

The Netherlands which is famous, for its beautiful tulips, is a very flat country. ☐

The Netherlands which is famous for its beautiful tulips, is a very flat country. ☐

1 mark

2. Place brackets around the parenthesis in these sentences. One has been done for you.

a) There was so much delicious food at the party (including my favourite dish of seafood pizza) that the guests were told to take some home with them.

b) Our window cleaner the one with red hair has gone on holiday for two weeks.

c) My old laptop the one I bought five years ago is very slow.   **2 marks**

3. Complete the sentences below by writing extra information in the dashes.

a) This dress – .... – is too small for me now.

b) Cheng – .... – plays rugby every weekend.

c) They ran to the edge of the pier – .... – and dropped their shells into the water.

3 marks

4. Tick one box to show which of these sentences correctly describes why we use parenthesis.

Tick **one.**

To divide a sentence into two clauses. ☐

To insert additional information into a sentence. ☐

To show where a sentence finishes. ☐

1 mark

Hyphens

1. Draw lines to match the words in the columns to form compound words. Write the compounds words below the table. One has been done for you.

> Hyphens are shorter than dashes and appear inside words. Sometimes they join a prefix with a word and sometimes they put two words together (a compound word).

man		biting
long		cold
half		eating
nail		distance
ice		eaten

man-eating, ...

.... 4 marks

2. Write three sentences using the compound words you have made in Question 1. One has been done for you.

a) A man-eating tiger was at large in the village. ....

b) ....

c) .... 2 marks

3. Underline the words in the passage below that should contain a hyphen. One has been done for you.

A swimming gala was held at the <u>openair</u> swimming pool last week. There were several categories of race to enter and I decided to compete in the hundredmetre race. My friend Howard entered the longdistance event. There was a crosssection of people of different ages at the event and everyone cooperated to make sure the gala ran on time. I didn't win but Howard did! I'm going to reenter next year. 5 marks

4. Write a sentence containing two hyphenated words.

....

.... 1 mark

Colons and semi-colons

1. Which of the sentences is punctuated correctly? *Colons are used to introduce lists or quotations.*

Tick **one.**

The car cleaners: valeted the car by washing it, vacuuming the interior and polishing the dashboard. ☐

The car cleaners valeted the car by: washing it, vacuuming the interior and polishing the dashboard. ☐

1 mark

2. Punctuate each sentence with a colon and commas.

a) Bradley keeps a lot of pets a dog a snake fifteen tropical fish and two parrots.

b) Mum packed my lunch box with tuna sandwiches an apple a packet of unsalted nuts and a small chocolate biscuit.

2 marks

3. Tick one box to show which sentence is correctly punctuated.

Tick **one.**

The orchard at the bottom of the fields; is great to play in I hope they never build on it. ☐

The orchard at the bottom of the fields is great to play in; I hope they never build on it. ☐

Semi-colons punctuate long lists of items that already have commas. They also divide two clauses in the same sentence.

1 mark

4. Punctuate each sentence with semi-colons (and colons and commas where needed). One has been done for you.

a) The snack bar served cola bangers and mash fish and chips bean burgers and mushy peas.

The snack bar served: cola; bangers and mash; fish and chips;

bean burgers and mushy peas.

b) There is so much to do to get the house ready for the party clean and polish the bathroom bake the cake make the sandwiches prepare the salad and chill the fruit juice.

....

.... **1 mark**

Apostrophes

1. Punctuate each sentence by adding the possessive apostrophe in the correct place. One has been done for you.

> Possessive apostrophes are used to show that something belongs to someone or something.

   a) Nina's children have all got blonde hair.

   b) Chantals garden has an old well in it.

   c) The womens clothing section is on the second floor of the department store.

   d) Rhyss jeans are torn.   **3 marks**

2. Write a sentence using a possessive apostrophe.

> Apostrophes are used to show where letters have been taken out when two words are shortened into one.

   .... **1 mark**

3. Rewrite the sentences, putting them into the contracted form. One has been done for you.

   a) You will know when you have arrived at the station because you will see all the lovely flower boxes.

   <u>You'll know when you've arrived at the station because you'll</u>

   <u>see all the lovely flower boxes.</u>

   b) I would like to go to Scotland in the holidays.

   ....

   ....

   c) You are coming on Saturday.

   ....

   ....

   d) We will help them to build the tree-house.

   ....

   .... **3 marks**

Punctuating speech

1. Tick one of the sentences below to show which is correctly punctuated.

Tick **one.**

> When you are writing in direct speech you use inverted commas to show the precise words that are spoken.

"My favourite writer is J K Rowling," said Naomi.   ☐

"My favourite writer is J K Rowling." said Naomi.   ☐

"My favourite writer is J K Rowling said," Naomi.   ☐

1 mark

2. Rewrite the sentences, showing the direct speech. Remember to punctuate your answer correctly. One has been done for you.

a) What wonderful news that is exclaimed Sheena

   "What wonderful news that is!" exclaimed Sheena. ....

b) Where is the entrance to the bowling alley asked Theresa

   ....

c) I have brought the washing in said Tom

   ....   **2 marks**

3. Which rule must you remember when a new speaker joins a conversation?

Tick **one.**

The new speaker should continue on the same line
as the original speaker.   ☐

Each new speaker should start on a new line.   ☐

1 mark

4. Using the rule you selected for Question 3 rewrite the conversation below.

"What are you going to wear for the concert?" asked Madeline. "I'm not sure," answered Yasmin, "maybe my new blue top and jeans." "I wish I could come too," said Mandy, "but my dad won't let me."

....

....

....

....

....   **3 marks**

Bullet points

1. Add one more bullet point to the list below.

To maintain dental hygiene and strong teeth you must:

- not eat too many sweets

- visit the dentist regularly

....

Bullet points are used to organise information in lists. The lead-in sentence usually ends in a colon.

1 mark

2. Rewrite the sentence below, using bullet points. Remember to punctuate your answer correctly.

In order to stay safe when you use the internet, you should never agree to meet anyone you don't know and trust, never share your personal details with anyone, always tell your parents or teacher if you receive anything that makes you feel uncomfortable, never open unknown attachments or links.

....

....

....

....

....   5 marks

3. Write bullet points, beginning with a lead sentence, setting out the things you should do to stay safe when cycling. Include at least three bullet points.

....

....

....

....

....   3 marks

Answers

GRAMMAR

1 Nouns

1. sun, sky, crows, rookery, trees, edge, village, Bishopthwaite, cawing, fields, rooftops, twigs, materials, nests, Simon, gate, binoculars, crows, chimpanzees, teacher

2. a), c), e)

3. Examples: street, distance, town, film, idea, tickets, weekend, bus, street, car, car, windscreen, fine, shock, film

2 Noun phrases

1. the long, slithering snake; a microscopic amount; this mirror

2. a) the time of the year that she loved
   b) the very last hill in the race
   c) Brilliant sunshine
   d) The woman who met us at the station … my friend's aunt.

3. Examples: b) my large, heavy, wet rucksack
   c) the glistening morning dew on the grass
   d) an old, battered, ticking clock

3 Pronouns

1. I, she, them, them, I, We, it, he, us, him, we, him

2. we, It, there, We, they

3. b) them c) it

4 Possessive pronouns

1. his, his, our, his, Her, his, mine, our

2. b) His bag is under the table.
   c) Their mother is in hospital.

3. b) mine. c) hers. d) theirs.

5 Relative pronouns

1. Relative pronoun: which, that, whose
   Possessive pronoun: his, mine, ours, theirs

2. a) whose b) where c) that d) which

3. whom, whose, which, where

6 Determiners

1. the, an, this, seven, every, your

2. Example: The, the/this, the, This, four, the, a, my/our, each/every, The

4. Last Saturday we went to **the** shopping mall in **the** centre of town. Ben needed new trainers so we went into **a** shop to look for them. **The** shop assistant said that they didn't have **his** size.

   I pointed to **a** shoe shop next door and said, "Let's look in **that** shop over there. It might have **your** size."

7 Conjunctions

1. but, if, When, so, then, and, After, and, when, so

2. a) because b) but c) and d) so

3. Examples: b) My sister is a very strong swimmer and she wants to swim the channel.
   c) Bharesh's laptop was running out of battery because he was playing so many games.

d) A new planet has been discovered at the edge of our solar system but it doesn't have a name yet.

8 Prepositions

1. c) The canal boat sailed **under** the bridge.

2. a) through b) before c) inside d) along e) during

3. For example, time: on, before
   place: over, in front of
   direction: towards, along

9 Adjectives

1. Adjective: heavenly, loud, lovely; Noun: pastry, weather

2. false, true, false

3. Examples: b) Shelley made a delicious, moist, chocolate cake for tea. c) The large, powerful and beautiful gorillas were in an enclosure in the centre of the wildlife park.
   d) The sunset spread across the peaceful hills.
   e) The trombone was in the untidy, cluttered, stuffy music room.

10 Present and past progressive tenses

1. Ted's favourite sport is judo.
   They are running onto to the pitch.

2. They are running onto to the pitch.

3. The vehicles were boarding the ferry. → past progressive
   He isn't in school today. → simple present
   The Tasmanian tiger became extinct in 1936. → simple past
   The luggage is coming down the conveyor belt now. → present progressive

11 Perfect tense

1. b) The band has just completed their tour.

2. a) Have you b) closed c) bought

3. a) so far b) before lunch c) when he came to stay

4. Tom will have borrowed a towel. → future perfect
   Tom had already borrowed a towel. → past perfect
   Tom has borrowed a towel. → present perfect

12 Auxiliary verbs

1. b) Do, do c) doesn't, be d) Did e) might f) were

2. am, are, has, be, did, can, do , is

a	s	x	h	d	o
m	r	v	y	i	s
f	b	e	l	d	m
v	d	x	c	a	n
h	a	s	r	m	o

13 Modal verbs

1. a) might b) can c) should d) would

2. The order is 3, 1, 4, 2

3. We must get to Dover before the ferry leaves →
   necessity
   You should save up to make sure you have enough money
   for the holidays → obligation
   My laptop crashed so it might not work anymore →
   possibility

14 Subjunctive verb forms

1. I suggest that she leave at the earliest opportunity.
   The school expects that all pupils be fully dressed in
   school uniform.

2. **b)** remain **c)** were

3. **a)** It is important that she brush her teeth every day.
   b) The headmaster insists that everyone wear a tie.
   c) Is it necessary that we also attend?
   d) It is important that he do his exercises every day.

15 Adverbs

1. adverb, adjective, adverb, adjective

2. perfectly, slowly, occasionally, eventually, securely,
   eagerly, swiftly, blindly, rapidly, abruptly

3. **b)** I'm sure Marsha didn't kick him deliberately.
   c) She dances gracefully.
   d) The crowd shouted defiantly.

16 Adverbials

1. **b)** in a tremendous hurry **c)** Once we had finished
   the picnic **d)** on the stroke of midnight **e)** Fiercely
   guarding her cubs

2. where, when, how

3. Just as I was falling asleep, the alarm clock rang.

17 Questions and statements

1. **a)** What is the longest river in Britain? **b)** He can't be
   right all of the time, can he? **c)** Nightingales are quite
   common in the woodland around here.

2. **a)** Chang, ski **b)** ponies, galloping **c)** caretaker, change

3. **b)** Ali was born on a Friday, wasn't he?
   c) Dame Kelly Holmes is a world renowned athlete,
   isn't she?

18 Commands and exclamations

1. **b)** Cut out the mask and paint it in bright colours.
   (command)
   c) Bring my shoes back here immediately! (command)
   d) What a clever dog he is! (exclamation)

2. **b)** Bring the fire extinguisher immediately!
   c) Place the ingredients in a bowl and mix well.
   d) How scary it would be to get lost here!

19 Subject and object

1. **a)** Poppy **b)** They **c)** She

2. **a)** the cups **b)** the puppies **c)** the plants

3. object, subject, object, object, subject

4. Everyone is going to the carnival.
   Children under 16 are not allowed to play the lottery.

20 Phrases

1. An arm and a leg, The long road home

2. **b)** with all that jam **c)** there's nothing nicer
   d) what a laugh **e)** on the table **f)** all in good time

3. **a)** on top of everything else **b)** out of nowhere
   c) how cool

21 Clauses

1. phrase, clause, phrase, phrase

2. **b)** we had an amazing time **c)** Ethan stayed awake
   until ten o'clock **d)** strawberry smoothies are a
   tasty snack **e)** I love reading in whatever form
   f) Matilde loves playing golf

22 Main and subordinate clauses

1. **b)** Whenever it snows, the whole community gathers
   at the top of the hill to go sledging. **c)** That family is
   very happy, despite the weather **d)** I love lilac flowers
   because they have a beautiful fragrance.
   e) If I were older, I would go travelling alone.

2. Sam called out to his mum → as she turned to go.
   The camels moaned and bared their teeth → while
   being coaxed to stand up.
   Noah is a talented pianist → even though he has
   fat fingers.
   Mia had lunch → before leaving the house.
   We won't know whether the play is good or not → until it
   takes place.

3. **b)** While being coaxed to stand up, the camels moaned
   and bared their teeth. **c)** Even though he has fat fingers,
   Noah is a talented pianist. **d)** Before leaving the house,
   Mia had lunch. **e)** Until it takes place, we won't know
   whether the play is good or not.

23 Coordinating conjunctions

1. **b)** yet **c)** so **d)** and **e)** or

2. and, for, so, or, yet, but, nor

a	x	c	n	k	a	a
z	n	t	o	r	w	b
q	g	d	r	u	l	u
l	f	x	e	y	e	t
z	s	m	f	y	v	p
f	o	r	c	l	q	p

3. **a)** but **b)** so **c)** or **d)** and

24 Subordinating conjunctions

1. **b)** until **c)** because **d)** while **e)** whenever

2. but (coordinating conjunction), or (coordinating conjunction),
   although (subordinating conjunction), once (subordinating
   conjunction), while (subordinating conjunction)

25 Relative clauses

1. **b)** Amena, who is seven years old
   c) Paris, where the Eiffel tower is located
   d) The restaurant at the end of the road, which is run by
   the Chen family,

2. The mangrove swamps → which
Yvonne Taylor → whose
In the woodland → where

3. Examples: **a)** held in Norway this year **b)** who is also his football coach **c)** where I went last year **d)** whose grandmother is 102 years old **e)** alongside the park

26 Active and passive

1. active, passive, active, passive

2. **b)** Emma's hair was trimmed by Helena. **c)** The hole in the wall was mended by Boris. **d)** The little boy's shoe laces were tied by Rahman.

27 Past tense

1. <u>Jed even said</u> that <u>it had been</u> an extremely long, boring day. One of the most boring days he could remember – until <u>it happened</u>. He and Lindon <u>had travelled</u> together on the number 16 bus as <u>they always did</u>. Jed gets on two stops before Lindon and always saves a seat for him at the back. Jed <u>was aimlessly playing</u> with his phone when <u>Lindon got on</u>. <u>School that day was</u> much the same as any on a wet Wednesday in November. <u>There were</u> the usual reprimands from Mr Johnson when <u>hardly anyone had done</u> their homework.

"<u>I have told</u> you a million times – you are not going to pass this exam by playing video games all evening!"

<u>The two boys ambled</u> through the school gate at four o'clock as usual. Instead of catching the bus <u>they decided</u> to walk home through the woodland at the back of school. As <u>they were coming</u> into the small clearing in the centre <u>they became</u> aware of a humming noise. <u>They looked up</u>, and there <u>it was</u>! <u>An immense spacecraft was taking off</u> over the treetops.

2. Examples:

   a) The past perfect tense: **it had been** an extremely long, boring day.

   b) The simple past tense: It **was** a very ordinary day.

   c) The present perfect tense: "**I have told** you a million times – you are not going to pass this exam by playing video games all evening!"

   d) The past progressive tense: Jed **was** aimlessly **playing** with his phone.

28 Future tense

1. Smudge is going to have puppies very soon, the puppies will be, Smudge will have a large litter, will be golden, some will be black, will be eight weeks old

2. We are having muffins for breakfast this Sunday.

   The washing up will have been done before Mum gets home.

   You will recognise us because we will be wearing purple T-shirts.

29 Standard English

1. non-standard English, Standard English, non-Standard English, Standard English, Standard English

2. **b)** Do you have **c)** Pupils are expected to **d)** I have been informed

3. **a)** It wasn't I who stole the sweets. **b)** He isn't going on holiday owing to his brother's illness. **c)** The shop keeper requested that everyone leave his shop.

PUNCTUATION

30 Capital letters and full stops

1. **a)** In March 1965, Mrs Beryl Thornberry swam across the English Channel to France. **b)** I have invited Lucas, Ben and Niamh to my party – I hope they can come. **c)** London is the capital of England and Rome is the capital of Italy.

2. true, false, true

3. I have swimming on Monday and football on Thursday so I am not available then. I can do Wednesday unless my sister has her French class.

4. Capital letters have not been used correctly and full stops are missing.

31 Question marks and exclamation marks

1. We always put glass bottles in the recycling bin → statement
What a fun party that was! → exclamation
How big is the population of Cardiff? → question

2. **a)** exclamation: What an amazing painting this is!

   b) statement: Tokyo is the capital of Japan.

   c) question: Do you like mangoes?

3. **b)** They visited Poland during the holidays, didn't they?
   c) Alan is very kind, isn't he?

32 Commas in lists

1. **b)** We took old pots and pans, clothes, bottles, jars and newspapers to the recycling centre. **c)** Dobry can play tennis, football, basketball and hockey. **d)** It was a cold, dark, depressing, grey day in January.

2. Diana is going to buy a litre of milk, six eggs, a tin of beans, one grapefruit and a loaf of bread.

3. There is a beautiful, vibrant peacock on the enormous, green lawn.

33 Commas for clarity

1. **a)** I love riding, tortoises, ice-cream, bicycles and swimming. **b)** Let's eat, Billy!

2. Swiftly closing the door behind her, Bryony ran into the garden.

3. Caitlin... → To mark the start and end of a relative clause.
After... → To mark the end of a fronted adverbial.
Although... → To mark the end of a subordinate clause.

4. **b)** Javier, who comes from Spain, can speak three languages. **c)** The Canadian state of Ontario, where you can visit the Niagara Falls, is heavily forested in some areas.

34 Parenthesis

1. The Netherlands, which is famous for its beautiful tulips, is a very flat country.

2. **b)** Our window cleaner (the one with red hair) has gone on holiday for two weeks. **c)** My old laptop (the one I bought five years ago) is very slow.

3. Examples:

   a) This dress – which I wore to my sister's wedding – is too small for me now.

   b) Cheng – a keen supporter of the All Blacks – plays rugby every weekend.

   c) They ran to the edge of the pier – pushing past several people – and dropped their shells into the water.

4. To insert additional information into a sentence.

35 Hyphens

1. long-distance, half-eaten, nail-biting, ice-cold

2. Examples: The marathon is a long-distance race.
The vampire's ice-cold skin was very pale.
Waiting for the results of the competition was a nail-biting experience.

3. hundredmetre, longdistance, crosssection, cooperated, reenter

4. Example: We train for long-distance swimming at my local open-air pool.

36 Colons and semi-colons

1. The car cleaners valeted the car by: washing it, vacuuming the interior and polishing the dashboard.

2. a) Bradley keeps a lot of pets: a dog, a snake, fifteen tropical fish and two parrots.

   b) Mum packed my lunch box with: tuna sandwiches, an apple, a packet of unsalted nuts and a small chocolate biscuit.

3. The orchard at the bottom of the fields is great to play in; I hope they never build on it.

4. b) There is so much to do to get the house ready for the party: clean and polish the bathroom; bake the cake; make the sandwiches; prepare the salad and chill the fruit juice.

37 Apostrophes

1. b) Chantal's garden has an old well in it.
   c) The women's clothing section is on the second floor of the department store. d) Rhys's jeans are torn.

2. Example: My school's Summer Fayre is being held on 25 June.

3. b) I'd like to go to Scotland in the holidays.
   c) You're coming on Saturday.
   d) We'll help them to build the tree-house.

38 Punctuating speech

1. "My favourite writer is J K Rowling," said Naomi.

2. b) "Where is the entrance to the bowling alley?" asked Theresa.
   c) "I have brought the washing in," said Tom.

3. Each new speaker should start on a new line.

4. "What are you going to wear for the concert?" asked Madeline.

   "I'm not sure," answered Yasmin, "maybe my new blue top and jeans."

   "I wish I could come too," said Mandy, "but my dad won't let me."

39 Bullet points

1. Example: floss your teeth.

2. In order to stay safe when you use the internet, you should:
   • never agree to meet anyone you don't know and trust
   • never share your personal details with anyone
   • always tell your parents or teacher if you receive anything that makes you feel uncomfortable
   • never open unknown attachments or links.

3. Example: To stay safe when cycling, you should:
   • always wear a helmet
   • follow the Highway Code
   • wear bright and visible clothing
   • be aware of other vehicles
   • signal clearly.

Published by Pearson Education Limited, 80 Strand, London, WC2R 0RL.

www.pearsonschools.co.uk

Text © Pearson Education Limited 2016
Edited by Jane Cotter
Typeset by Jouve India Private Limited
Produced by Elektra Media
Original illustrations © Pearson Education Limited 2016
Illustrated by Elektra Media
Cover illustration by Ana Albero

The right of Helen Thomson to be identified as author of this work has been asserted by her in accordance with the Copyright, Designs and Patents Act 1988.

First published 2016

ARP Impression 98

British Library Cataloguing in Publication Data
A catalogue record for this book is available from the British Library.

ISBN 978 1 292 14594 5

Copyright notice
All rights reserved. No part of this publication may be reproduced in any form or by any means (including photocopying or storing it in any medium by electronic means and whether or not transiently or incidentally to some other use of this publication) without the written permission of the copyright owner, except in accordance with the provisions of the Copyright, Designs and Patents Act 1988 or under the terms of a licence issued by the Copyright Licensing Agency, Barnard's Inn, 86 Fetter Lane, London EC4A 1EN (www.cla.co.uk). Applications for the copyright owner's written permission should be addressed to the publisher.

Printed in Great Britain by Ashford Colour Press ltd.